Growing Up Gullah in the Lowcountry

Josie Olsvig

Palmetto Publishing Group

Charleston, SC

Growing Up Gullah in the Lowcountry
Copyright © 2020 by Josie Olsvig

First Edition

Printed in the United States

ISBN-13 978-1-64111-402-8
ISBN-10: 1-64111-402-9

My name is Veronica. I live with my mother and my two brothers in a small house in Mount Pleasant, near Charleston, South Carolina. I have family living all around me in nearby homes, and we all have the same big yard. Our distant grandfather was an enslaved African-American; he was given this land in the 1860s, after the Civil War. We all live on what is known as heirs' property. Some freemen were very lucky and received forty acres of land, while others had to buy it. They had to carefully save their earnings to purchase parcels of land.

From the late 1600s until the mid-1800s, a period of time called the antebellum period, meaning before the Civil War, members of our family lived on big plantations which looked like huge farms. They grew crops like rice, cotton, tea, and a plant called indigo. Indigo was used to add blue coloring to clothes. It was also used as a blue paint around windows and door frames to keep bad spirits, or haints, away. In England, the coloring was used in the textile industry, particularly in making robes for royalty.

Our family is Gullah or Geechee. This is both a culture and a Creole language. The Gullah language is part English and a variety of West African languages. Most Gullah people came from the West African countries of Sierra Leone, Gambia, Guinea, Liberia, and Senegal. These people possessed important skills in growing rice. The Carolina gold rice was a money-making cash crop for South Carolina back in the 1700s and 1800s.

Grammy told me we are called "binyas." It's a Gullah term for a person who is from the Lowcountry. It means "been here." While tourists or others who move to the area are called a "comya," meaning that they have "come here" from somewhere else.

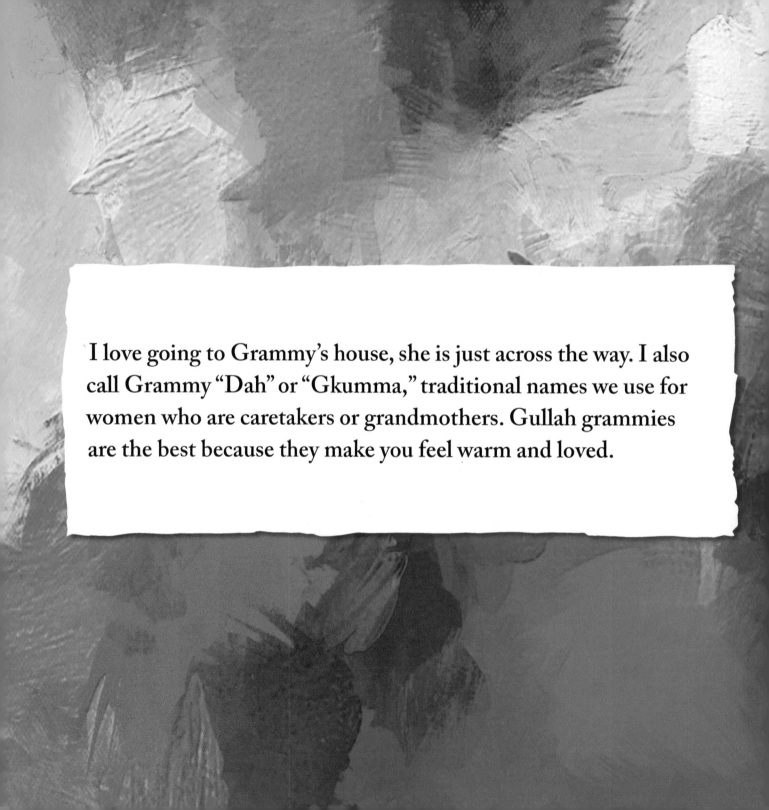

I love going to Grammy's house, she is just across the way. I also call Grammy "Dah" or "Gkumma," traditional names we use for women who are caretakers or grandmothers. Gullah grammies are the best because they make you feel warm and loved.

Yesterday morning Grammy and I were sitting on her front porch. We snapped peas for dinner as we rocked in the big rocking chairs and talked about what it was like growing up in our town of Mount Pleasant, South Carolina. It is located right across from the city of Charleston, an old city that dates back to the 1600s.

Grammy said that our family has held our property for over a hundred and fifty years now, since shortly after the Civil War. Most people, like my distant grandfather, used to farm the land to support their families. Nowadays, the property can be used by anyone who is kin to my great-great-great-grandpa. Heirs' property is special like that, it belongs to many family members.

Grammy and I do a lot of things together because she says I am her best helper. She said that the family kitchen didn't always look like it does today. They didn't get a stove until 1959. Before that they cooked near the fireplace and allowed the smoke to go up the chimney. Around that same time, they switched from using oil lamps to electric lights. They also switched from chilling butter in the backyard water well to cooling it in a refrigerator so it hardens.

Our big yard is a wonderful place. We have several palmetto trees; they look similar to a palm tree, but are shorter and have big fan-shaped clusters of leaves. We also have a big oak tree. Grammy said it is nearly three hundred years old. Light gray moss hangs from the oak tree; it's called Spanish moss. But it's not Spanish or a moss. It lives on moisture and nutrients in the air. We also have Southern magnolia, Confederate jasmine, wisteria, and four o'clock bushes. They are beautiful and smell so good!

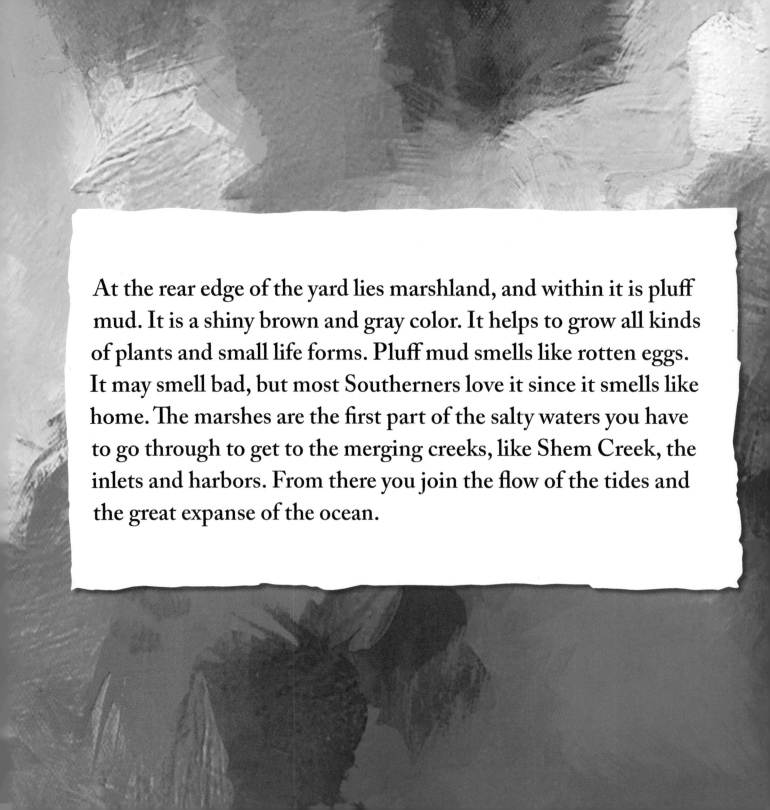

At the rear edge of the yard lies marshland, and within it is pluff mud. It is a shiny brown and gray color. It helps to grow all kinds of plants and small life forms. Pluff mud smells like rotten eggs. It may smell bad, but most Southerners love it since it smells like home. The marshes are the first part of the salty waters you have to go through to get to the merging creeks, like Shem Creek, the inlets and harbors. From there you join the flow of the tides and the great expanse of the ocean.

Charleston is located on the Atlantic Ocean. Two rivers, the Cooper and the Ashley, create a peninsula, and the city is at the tip of it. Mount Pleasant is across the Cooper River from Charleston. For a long time, the only way to get to Charleston from Mount Pleasant was by ferry. Then around 1929 a steel bridge was built, Grace Memorial Bridge. In 1946 a freighter hit the bridge, causing a lot of damage. It became unsafe and eventually it was torn down. Now we have a beautiful new bridge, the Ravenel Bridge, that allows us to go easily from Mt. Pleasant down to Charleston.

Charleston is an important city and a very historic one. The Civil War began and ended in this city. The first shots of the war were fired in April 1861 at Fort Sumter, an old fort located in the waters by the Charleston peninsula. This is right across from the Battery, where there is a park and where the old cannons still sit.

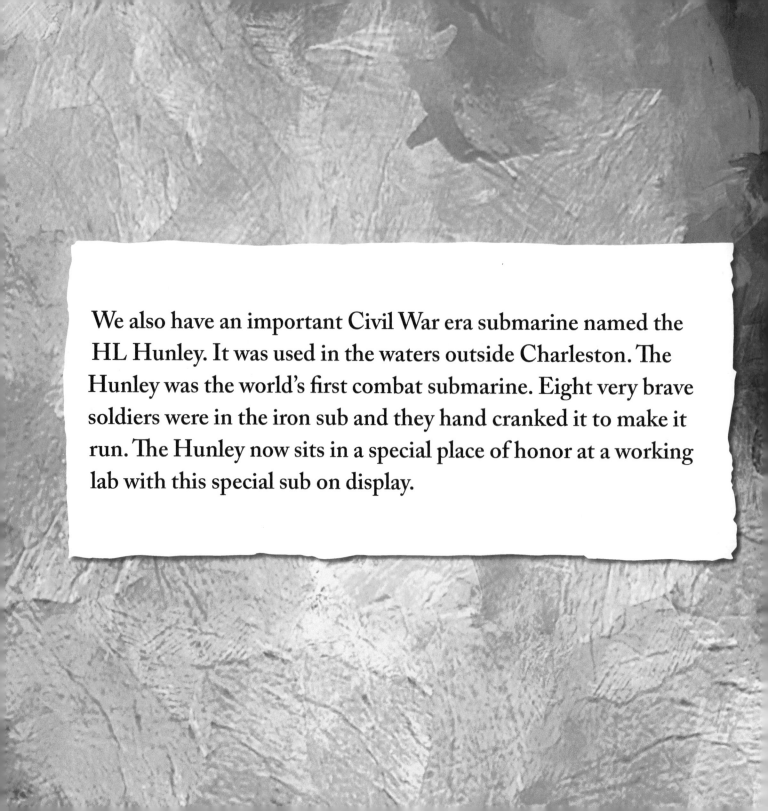

We also have an important Civil War era submarine named the HL Hunley. It was used in the waters outside Charleston. The Hunley was the world's first combat submarine. Eight very brave soldiers were in the iron sub and they hand cranked it to make it run. The Hunley now sits in a special place of honor at a working lab with this special sub on display.

Another important event occurred in Charleston during the Civil War involving an enslaved African-American man named Robert Smalls. As a young man, he worked on a Confederate ship called the Planter. He had been hired out by his slave owner in Beaufort, South Carolina. Robert Smalls was a very brave and smart man. He figured out how he, his family, and his crew could seize the ship he worked on and sail it to the safety of Union ships and gain their freedom. He seized the ship the Planter and sailed it to the Union side of the harbor. Eventually, he became a Union ship captain, the first Black captain of an army ship, and, ultimately, a United States Congressman. He served five terms in that office.

ROBERT SMALLS

The custom of making sweetgrass baskets can be traced back through our heritage in Africa. Making these baskets is a Gullah tradition of over three hundred years that our ancestors learned when they lived in West Africa. Grammy makes sweetgrass baskets, and so does my mama. Grammy says that a long time ago only men made these baskets, but now it's mainly women. Dried sweetgrass is bundled together and coiled in circles. Thin strands of palmetto fronds hold the pieces in place, and bulrush and pine needles are then woven in for decoration and strength.

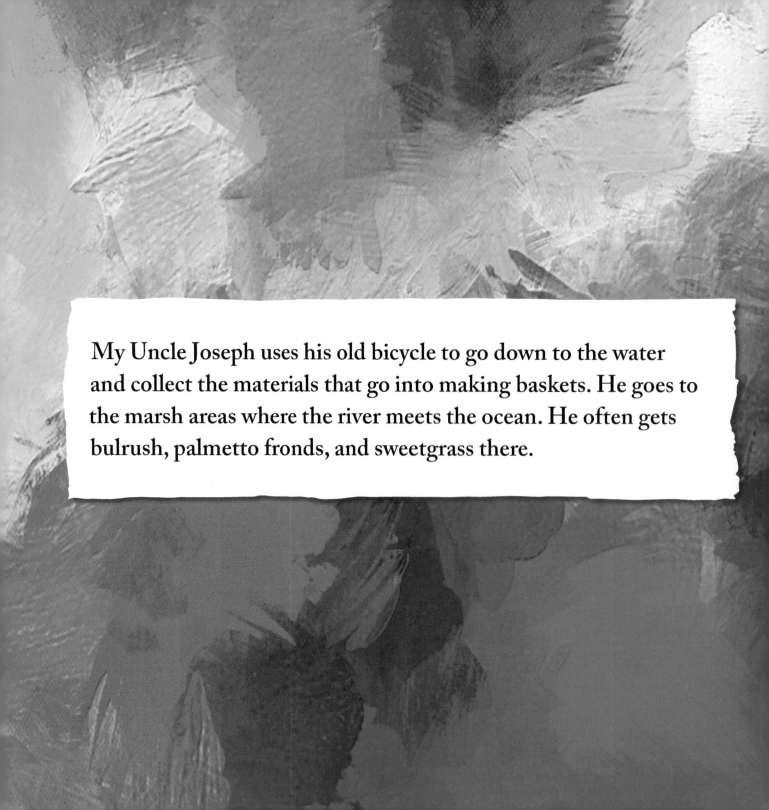

My Uncle Joseph uses his old bicycle to go down to the water and collect the materials that go into making baskets. He goes to the marsh areas where the river meets the ocean. He often gets bulrush, palmetto fronds, and sweetgrass there.

Grammy showed me the sewing bone she uses to make these pretty sweetgrass baskets. Sewing bones are sharpened metal spoons. She said some people also use what is called a "nailbone." They are little metal picks made by flattening nails or whittling the rib bones of a cow or pig. We have lots of friends and relatives that sell the baskets all around our town of Mount Pleasant. Basket makers often use special stands to sell them.

You can also see sweetgrass basket vendors in the City Market in downtown Charleston. The original City Market was built in the early 1800s on land that was donated by Charles Cotesworth Pinckney, a local wealthy landowner and politician. The current building was completed in 1841. Originally, only vegetables, meat, and fish were sold there, but now all kinds of goods can be purchased at the City Market, especially the beautiful sweetgrass baskets.

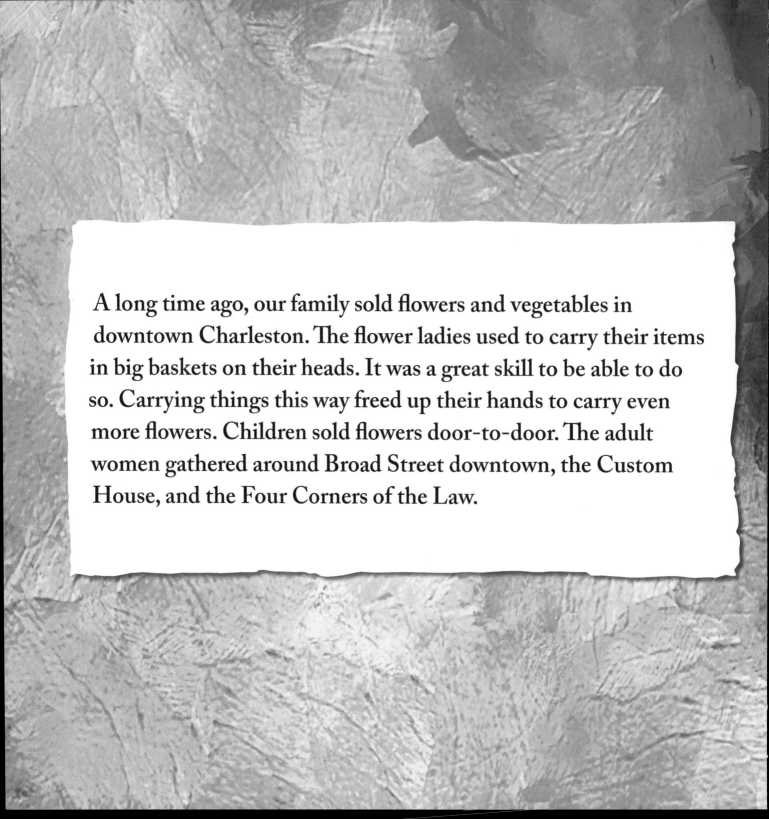

A long time ago, our family sold flowers and vegetables in downtown Charleston. The flower ladies used to carry their items in big baskets on their heads. It was a great skill to be able to do so. Carrying things this way freed up their hands to carry even more flowers. Children sold flowers door-to-door. The adult women gathered around Broad Street downtown, the Custom House, and the Four Corners of the Law.

The first school in Charleston for African-American children was the Avery Normal Institute, founded right after the Civil War, in 1865. Initially, the institute taught elementary and high school levels, but it later took on the preparation of young teachers. Back then, schools that taught young adults how to become teachers were called "normal schools."

Since early in United States' history, African-American slaves were not allowed to learn how to read or write. South Carolina had been the first state to pass laws forbidding it, and so it was important to teach newly freed slaves these skills along with basic math. They needed this knowledge in order to manage a household, to understand budgeting, and to learn a trade so they could live independently.

The Avery Normal Institute was established by missionaries from New York, the American Missionary Association or "AMA." It was a very progressive school and only took the best students. The Avery has accomplished many achievements in the one hundred and fifty years it has been in existence. However, one of the more important ones is that teachers and students there helped to establish the first chapter of the NAACP in the State of South Carolina, in 1917. After that, Avery students and staff fought to desegregate the schools in the 1960s and participated in a 1969 hospital strike asking for fair wages for workers.

Most of the people in my family attended a school in Mount Pleasant called the Laing School. Initially, the Laing School was a high school for African-American students only. Like the Avery Institute, it was founded shortly after the Civil War. It also taught recently freed slaves basic reading, writing and arithmetic along with a trade, such as wood-working or shoemaking.

The Gullah culture has a variety of herbal remedies, used for generations. Grammy told me about these special healing medicines and botanicals that she learned of as a young girl. Many people make these medicines at home. The remedies are made from things like roots, leaves, berries, tree bark, and herbs. She gives me some of these teas and rubs, like the herb Life Everlasting, when I have a cold.

On special days, Grammy and I go down to the water and watch the waves roll in. Grammy says that the Gullah people have always lived near the water. They have fished and collected shrimp and crab in their big nets. Grammy says we have kin that live down in the Barrier Islands near Beaufort, SC, and Savannah, Georgia. Those places are also located on the Atlantic Ocean, just like Mount Pleasant and Charleston. Down by the water, there are also special birds like the snowy white egrets, peregrine falcons, kingfishers, and great blue herons. These great birds are beautiful.

On Sundays, we always go to church as a family. We go to the Goodwill AME Church on Route 17. AME stands for African Methodist Episcopal Church. Grandma says that a long time ago our family had to sing our praises to God or "dance the shout" in a building called a praise house. That was before Gullah people had churches like we have today.

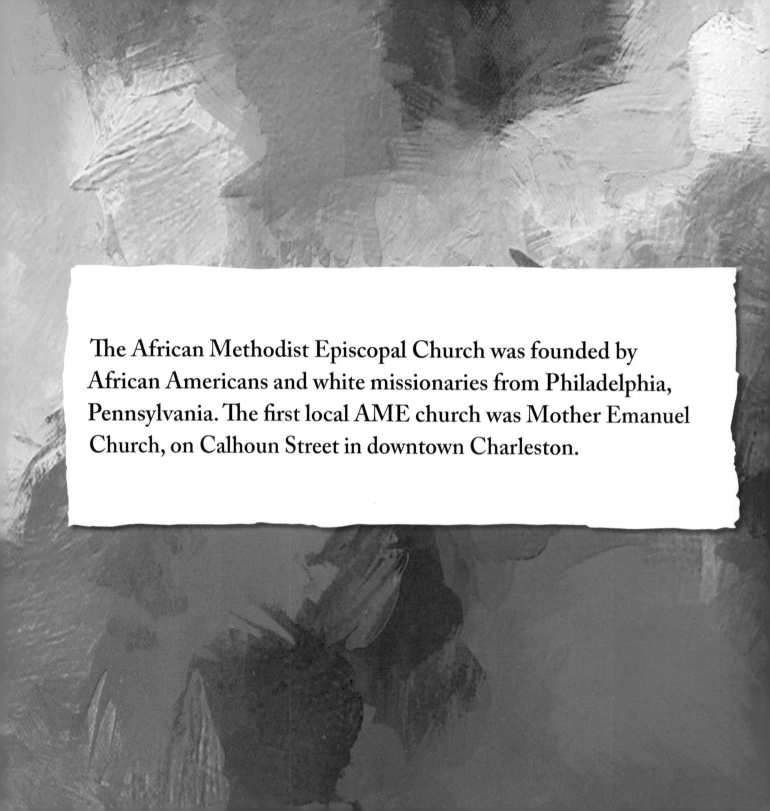

The African Methodist Episcopal Church was founded by African Americans and white missionaries from Philadelphia, Pennsylvania. The first local AME church was Mother Emanuel Church, on Calhoun Street in downtown Charleston.

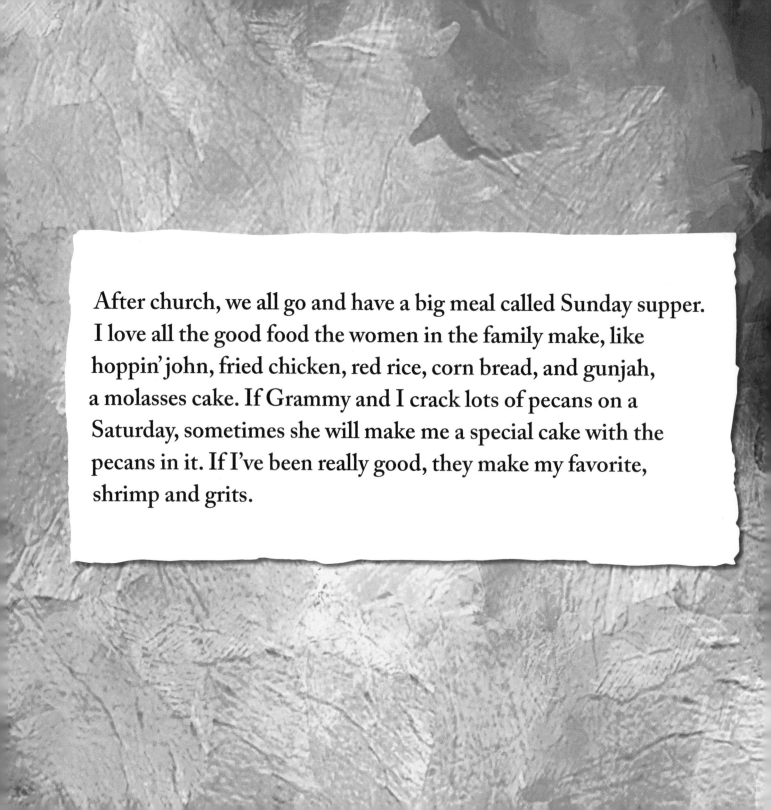

After church, we all go and have a big meal called Sunday supper.
I love all the good food the women in the family make, like
hoppin' john, fried chicken, red rice, corn bread, and gunjah,
a molasses cake. If Grammy and I crack lots of pecans on a
Saturday, sometimes she will make me a special cake with the
pecans in it. If I've been really good, they make my favorite,
shrimp and grits.

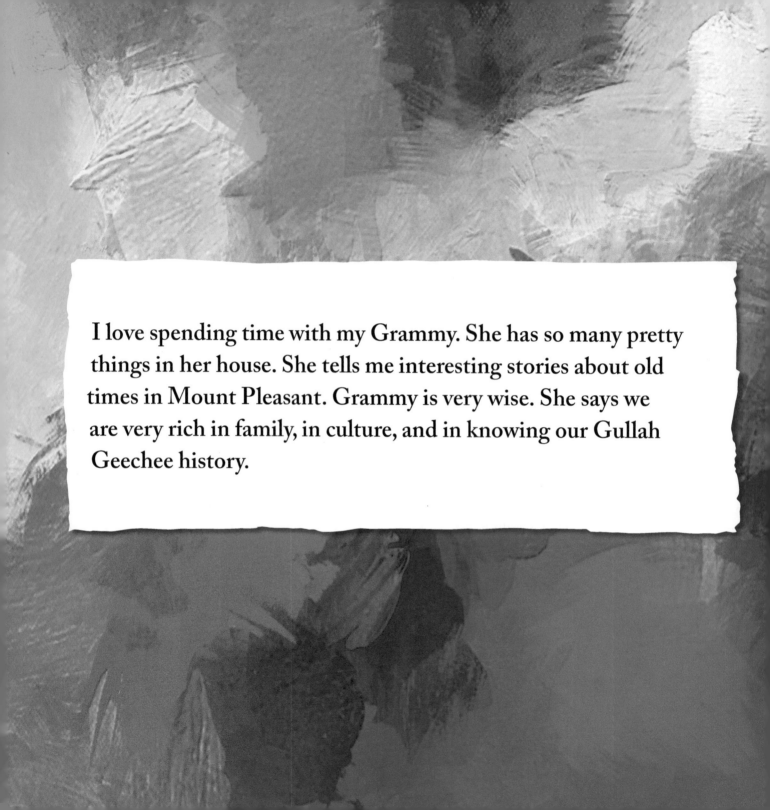

I love spending time with my Grammy. She has so many pretty things in her house. She tells me interesting stories about old times in Mount Pleasant. Grammy is very wise. She says we are very rich in family, in culture, and in knowing our Gullah Geechee history.

Information for the Parent or Teacher

When the Civil War commenced, there were four million slaves living in the United States. Roughly 400,000 of them lived in South Carolina. African Americans, both enslaved and free, made up 57 percent of the state's population. This high concentration was largely attributable to Charleston being the country's largest port of slave trade, the city where many of the enslaved people first landed. Over 40 percent of all enslaved African Americans came through this port of entry.

Charleston was built on slave labor and, for nearly 200 years, thrived under a slave economy. Many of the notable buildings in Charleston, including Rainbow Row, were built with slave labor. It was not where the first slaves landed, but is believed that this is where slavery saw its greatest proliferation. It is also where the heart of the pro-slavery movement took hold and the ideals of a separate nation evolved, first as the Confederacy, then later sought as a collection of nation-states in the Golden Circle. The Knights of the Golden Circle advanced the idea of creating their own new pro-slavery country composed of the seceded states, Mexico, Central America, and the Caribbean. The Knights followed the protocols and customs of the Masons while promoting their notion to perpetuate slavery.

The Gullah Corridor

The history of the Gullah people goes back over three hundred years on the South-eastern coast of America. This cohesive group of people formed a culture and a language known as the Gullah or Geechee. Generally, North Carolina and South Carolina use the term Gullah, whereas southward toward Georgia and Florida the term Geechee is used. The recognized region they inhabit extends at its most northern point from Wilmington,

North Carolina, and Cape Fear southward toward Northern Florida near Jacksonville. It encompasses all of the Sea Islands and approximately thirty-five miles inland to the St. John's River. This region has been identified by the federal government as the Gullah/Geechee Corridor. The African Americans in this region are the descendants of former slaves brought to this country from the western coast of Africa.

Special Skills Brought to America

Many of the slaves brought to the Charleston area possessed particular skills in growing rice, a difficult and complicated plant to grow due to its differing requirements in planting and cultivation. African rice is related to Asian rice, yet it is a distinct species. Once it was discovered it could grow in the American South, slaves knowledgeable about rice were actively sought out. Rice had been grown in their native Africa for over two thousand years, so a reliable body of knowledge evolved for the Gullah people. They knew how to develop and build irrigation systems, dams and earthworks, something previously unknown to plantation owners of European decent.

Gullah is a Creole Language

The language and manner of speaking which evolved among the Gullah was a mixture of African terms, melody of the language, movement, and nature of expression, coupled with British English. At first it was referred to as "bad English," but over time it has become recognized as its own dialect. It is a creole language. This, however, took decades to be realized.

Capture in Africa and Travel in Slave Ships

The Gullah people were brought to a foreign land against their will where they initially did not speak the language or understand the culture and style of dress. Over time, they merged the customs and style of life as adopted from the British settlers along with their own culture. While there were many differences, there were also similarities, particularly with regard to values and core beliefs. This helped them to adapt to life in America. Both societies had structure, a hierarchy, and a respectful regard for authority figures. Both believed in the strength of a family unit and in loyalty to the family. Both cultures knew and appreciated the difference between right and wrong. All of this helped the slaves of the antebellum South to assimilate into Southern culture. However, this assimilation did not come without great strife and pain.

The slaves were captured in their native Africa for mercenary reasons, so that slave traders could make large sums of money. After being ambushed and taken captive, they were forced to walk from the interior of Africa to the coast, where they met awaiting slave ships. These captives were chained or held in irons and packed into the holds of slave ships like sardines. While on board, for the most part they could not turn or shift their bodies. They were forced to lie in the supine position for hours or days at a time. The captives were forced into overcrowded ships saturated with the stench of death and human waste. It is difficult to comprehend just how bad this trip was; it took an average of about seventy days. Some of the captives died during their violent capture or while walking the many miles to the coast. Yet others died on board the ship due to disease. Some chose death, believing that their spirit would return to their homeland of Africa. Due to the practice of jumping overboard, as well as throwing the dead overboard, it was not uncommon for sharks to follow the slave ships in anticipation of a quick and easy meal.

The Roots of Southern Cooking

While the newly enslaved were unable to bring personal possessions, they had memories. They could practice their arts, language, agricultural know-how, culinary skills, oral tradition, and spirituality. These elements streamed into the Gullah culture and enabled it to flourish. When we think of "Southern cooking," much of it is an amalgamation of American elements, such as butter and cream, along with African foods, such as okra, rice, watermelon, sorghum, black eyed peas, and yams.

Faith and the Founding of Mother Emanuel AME Church

Christianity was not introduced to enslaved African Americans in earnest until around 1830, while spotty efforts started before that. Slave masters thought that imparting Christian ideals would help reinforce acceptance of the slaves' station in life and obedience to the master's rule. Those enslaved identified with the people of Egypt and others who had been similarly oppressed. They drew on the concept of a just reward in heaven for their suffering here on earth. It was initially the Methodists, then the Baptists, that shared Christian concepts with the Gullah. In turn, they selectively borrowed concepts to create their own folk religion. It was spirituality rather than strict Christian doctrine that became the Gullah's foundation. They used both Christian relics and African spiritual items.

As time went on, African-American churches were formed throughout the South. In Charleston, the first such church was the Emanuel African Methodist Episcopal Church, better known as Mother Emanuel AME Church. It is the oldest AME church in the South, having been founded in 1816. It is the church in which a young South Carolinian shooter gunned down nine church members, adults and children alike, during Bible study. Despite this tragedy, the church, its parish, and the surrounding community pulled together to overcome the pain and heartache caused by the massacre. A stronger and more united Charleston has resulted.

Questions for Discussion

1. Who are the Gullah people?

2. Where do they live?

3. What type of work did they do on antebellum plantations or large farms?

4. Did they live and work in places other than plantations?

5. What did you think was the most interesting part of the story?

   Why?

6. What war was fought in Charleston in the 1860s?

7. What kind of baskets do the Gullah people make in Charleston and Mount Pleasant?

8. What is pluff mud?

9. What or who was the HL Hunley?

10. How did education change for enslaved African-Americans after the Civil War?

CPSIA information can be obtained
at www.ICGtesting.com
Printed in the USA
LVHW071623250421
685525LV00001B/10

9 781641 114028

3 1901 04549 8567